THE NON-ELECTRIC LIGHTING SERIES

BOOK 8: Alcohol Mantle Lamps

Ron Brown

R&C Publishing

Newark Valley, New York

Notice: This manual is designed to provide information on alcohol-fueled mantle lamps and lanterns.

It is not the purpose of this guide to reprint all the information that is otherwise available, but to complement, amplify, and supplement other texts and resources. You are urged to read all the available material and learn as much as you can about alcohol lamps and lanterns and to tailor the information to your specific circumstances.

Every effort has been made to make this guide as complete and accurate as possible. However, there may be mistakes, both typographical and in content. Therefore this text should be used only as a general guide and not as the ultimate source of alcohol mantle-lamp information. Furthermore, this guide contains information that is current only up to the printing date.

The purpose of this manual is to educate and entertain. The views, opinions, positions, and strategies expressed by the author are his alone. The author makes no representations as to the accuracy, completeness, correctness, suitability, or validity of any information in this book and will not be liable for any errors, omissions, or delays in this information or any losses, injuries, or damages arising from its use.

ISBN 978-0-9970228-2-7

Published by R&C Publishing
15 Dr. Knapp Road South
Newark Valley, NY 13811

Printed in the United States of America

Table of Contents

FOREWORD

This is the eighth book in The Non-Electric Lighting Series. I have to admit that it gave me a start to realize that I will have written seven of the eight Forewords. Plus the Foreword to both of Ron Brown's 2000-hour flashlight books. There has been a lot of writing going on – not so much me, but by Ron. What a gift he has created!

So what is left to say? After all those introductory remarks, I realized that, as I sat down to write this, I was at a loss for words. What could I say that has not already been said?

I suppose I can start with the fact that Ron recently changed the cover photo on his Facebook page to show off his lighting books. They are spread out like a hand of playing cards. I learned that one of his friends (who happens to be a bluegrass banjo picker) saw that cover and commented, "Expecting trouble, Ron?"

And the answer came back:

"Of course. Do you remember the Alan Jackson/Jimmy Buffett song, "It's Five O'clock Somewhere"? Well, it's always five o'clock somewhere and there's always a blackout somewhere. And how ya gonna play your banjo in the dark if you drop your pick?"

Indeed. There is always a blackout somewhere. It might be local and affect just your city. Or it could be huge, covering a wide geographical area. In a worst case scenario it could be a massive, humongous event that affects the entire continent. I am thinking EMP event (electromagnetic pulse) or cyberattack on the grid. It could happen and if it did, we would be without power for a long, long time. Perhaps for life.

Regardless of the cause, be it weather, war, or an EMP, there is always a blackout somewhere and we better be prepared.

Alcohol mantle lamps, the topic of this book, produce light on par with a 100-watt electric light bulb. And alcohol, not being a petroleum product, can be produced locally, like moonshine whiskey. That is what happened in Europe during WWII. With petroleum rationing, did you know that high-proof bootleg was produced and used in lamps and lanterns? Some might think that was a waste; I consider it resourceful!

It is important to know that with a bit of alcohol, you do not have to work by candlelight even in the worst of times. You can have the equivalent of a 100-watt light bulb and this book will show you how. Or, as Ron might say, it reveals "how ya' do the doin'."

As with all of Ron's books in the Non-Electric Lighting Series, I suggest you read Alcohol Mantle Lamps then tuck it away for future reference. You just never know when you might need it.

Gaye Levy
December 2015

"Let there be light . . ." (Genesis 1:3)

INTRODUCTION

Were you to ask a group of American preppers or survivalists to name some lantern fuels, no doubt Coleman fuel, propane, and kerosene would top the list (all of which are petroleum products). I suspect *alcohol* wouldn't even be on the list.

But alcohol is probably the ultimate survival fuel. You can grow some vegetables (vodka is made from potatoes, for example); ferment a mash-wort-wine from the fruit; distill the 'wine' to concentrate the alcohol; and burn the resulting high-proof bootleg in a mantle lamp. That's what the Europeans did during World War Two. You can use grain, too. Bourbon is made from corn. Scotch is made from barley. Rye is made from rye.

In a less extreme scenario (a simple power outage or blackout), alcohol can supply a solution that few people know exists. When the next Big Storm is forecast and shoppers prowl Walmart chasing down the last gallon of Coleman fuel or the last propane cylinder, you can stroll over to the drugstore section and grab some rubbing alcohol (isopropyl). It's right next to the vitamins. Or you can head back to automotives and pick up some dry gas (methanol). Or to hardware and get some shellac thinner (denatured alcohol). What part of smiley-face don't you understand? ☺

Alcohol, as a fuel, has other advantages over petroleum products. For one thing, it doesn't degrade in storage. For another, it produces virtually no carbon monoxide compared to petroleum products; alcohol is the safest energy source for inside use as regards carbon monoxide.

Consider this. Radius Engineering of Forney, Texas builds prefab fiberglass shelters to protect against NBC attacks (nuclear, biological, chemical). The shelters are installed underground (which means air circulation is always a concern). The kitchens in these shelters feature built-in alcohol-burning stoves. Why? They produce less carbon monoxide than anything else.

• The first section of this book will cover basic lamp theory. There's both terminology and concepts we need to get under our belt before meaningful discussion can take place. Kinds of alcohol (methanol, ethanol, denatured, and isopropyl). Combustible versus flammable. How mantles work. Stuff like that.

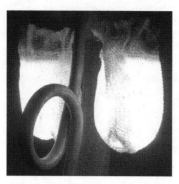

■ **ABOVE:** *Alcohol burns with a nearly invisible flame. But the heat from that flame causes a mantle to incandesce. That's where the light comes from.* ■

● The second section of this book discusses some early European alcohol lamps. *Mantle* lamps, let us be clear, not Gilbert-chemistry-set lab burners with a candle-size flame.

■ **ABOVE:** *This is a lab-type alcohol lamp. Because you can barely see an alcohol flame, this lamp, for demo purposes, is burning kerosene.* ■

13

The purpose of discussing European lamps is to validate alcohol as a lamp fuel and alcohol mantle lamps as producing useful quantities of light. Alcohol-as-lamp-fuel is a forgotten technology in this country. Well, not forgotten, really. It was never known in the first place. In Europe, back in the day, there were several brands of alcohol lamps. In America, back in the day, there were NO brands of alcohol lamps. Americans lived in the shadow of Standard Oil and General Motors.

• The third section is the heart of the book. It contains detailed instructions for converting a Coleman Quick-Lite table lamp to alcohol. Admittedly, the Quick-Lite is an antique; you can't buy one new. But it's not overly rare.

Our converted Quick-Lite will produce 100 watts-worth of light. Complexity-wise, the task is on par with a high school shop project. You'll need a drill, some needlenose pliers, tinsnips, and a steady hand. It's my own little invention and it works quite nicely, thank you.

How about safety? After all, the Coleman Quick-Lite was designed for white gas (Coleman fuel), not alcohol.

In answer, what we're going to do is install a butterfly valve in the air intake tube to regulate the amount of air going to the flame. Doing so will allow us to tune in a fuel-air ratio that's alcohol-friendly. Alcohol needs less air than white gas.

After that, substituting *flammable* alcohol for *flammable* white gas is akin to swapping oak firewood for maple firewood. A converted Quick-Lite table lamp on alcohol is just as safe as it is on Coleman fuel.

● The fourth section of this book describes two other alcohol conversions (the Petromax 150CP and the Leacock 107). Neither produces results as good as the Quick-Lite but it's nice to know that alternatives exist.

■ **ABOVE:** *A Petromax 150CP lantern.* ■

■ **ABOVE:** *A brand new Leacock Model 107 with stainless steel font.* ■

• The fifth and last section discusses safety (oxygen starvation and carbon monoxide).

• What we will *not* cover in this book is the home manufacture of alcohol a.k.a. moonshine or bootleg. Only commercially available alcohols will be discussed. Even so, it's nice to understand the principle involved:

Water boils at 212° F. If you boil some water on the stove, the vapor given off will condense on any surface that is below 212° F (the pan cover, for example) and turn back into a liquid.

Alcohol boils at 173° F. So if the moonshiner heats his mash-wort-wine to above 173° but holds it below 212°, the alcohol will boil off and leave the water behind. Then if he passes the alcohol vapor over a cold surface it will condense and drip into a Mason jar . . . *White lightnin'!*

17

THEORY

Kinds of Alcohol

Alcohol and the chemistry thereof can get very complicated very quickly. So I'm going to follow the KISS principle in this discussion. KISS is an acronym for 'Keep It Simple, Stupid.'

Hey! I resemble that remark.

- *Methanol* is 'wood alcohol' (made from wood chips) and is poisonous. 'Heet' is one brand of methanol, used to start cars in the winter. You'll find it in the automotive section of Walmart. Methanol should be handled with care because it's readily absorbed through the skin.

- *Ethanol* is 'grain alcohol' (made from grain) and is drinkable. You'll find it in liquor stores. But drinkable means taxable and taxable means expensive. So I'm going to ignore ethanol and pretend that it's not on the list.

Even so, we should understand 'proof' and 'percent.' In the USA, the proof number of hard liquor is simply the percent number doubled. Eighty proof Jack Daniel's bourbon, for example, is 40% alcohol. Sierra Silver brand 150-proof tequila is 75% alcohol.

• *Denatured alcohol* is ethanol with some methanol added (making it poisonous, undrinkable, nontaxable, and cheap). Denatured alcohol is sold by the gallon in hardware stores. It's used as shellac thinner and as fuel in marine stoves.

• *Isopropyl* (also non-drinkable) is rubbing alcohol. The most common isopropyl is 70% alcohol (30% water) but 91% isopropyl (9% water) is also available. You'll find both in Walmart's drugstore section. The 70% variety can be lit with a match and will burn but will not get hot enough to incandesce a mantle. The stuff you need as lamp fuel is 91%. Oddly (or so it seems to me), its use as rubbing alcohol notwithstanding, isopropyl is absorbed through the skin.

*****

Your body can accommodate small amounts of methanol, denatured, and isopropyl alcohol (whether inhaled or absorbed through the skin) but poisoning can occur if an excess builds up to the point your liver can't handle the load. But that's true of ethanol, the drinkable stuff, as well, eh?

For the chemically inclined, please know that alcohol mixes perfectly with water. It is *miscible* in water; no *meniscus* forms between the alcohol and the water. (Oh good. That clears everything up.)

Mantles

Mantle lamps are different. Just as the tungsten filament in an electric bulb 'incandesces' or glows from the heat of the electric current passing through the wire, so a mantle in a non-electric lamp incandesces from a flame's heat. The light produced by the mantle is many times brighter than the light from the flame itself.

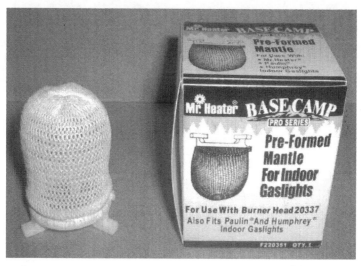

■ **ABOVE:** *Pre-formed mantles come in a variety of shapes and sizes. Right out of the box they are rigid, pre-shaped, and pre-fastened to some sort of mounting fixture. Antique French Tito-Landi alcohol lamps use preformed mantles but they are tall and skinny, quite different in shape from what's pictured here).* ■

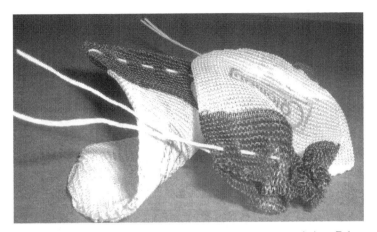

■ **ABOVE:** *Flexible 'sock-style' mantles are used by Primus alcohol lanterns (Swedish) as well as Coleman Quick-Lite table lamps. Sock-style mantles resemble miniature drawstring bags. There is only one opening. It fits over the end of the burner tube. The mantles are hand-tied in place. Once fired, the mantles become rigid.* ■

A 1922 Coleman ad said their mantles were made from "long-fibre Egyptian cotton." In later years, cotton was superseded by rayon.

The woven cloth mantle is soaked in a rare-earth solution, then coated with lacquer. It's the rare earth that glows and produces light. The cloth is only a carrier. Before using the mantle the first time, we burn away the lacquer and cloth. The ash skeleton left behind is what incandesces and generates light.

Throughout most of the 1900's, thorium was the rare earth used in mantles. Thorium, however, is faintly radioactive (making it a hot-button issue). In the politically-correct 1980's, thorium mantles were largely (not totally) replaced with yttrium, a rare earth that is not radioactive.

Please know that old-time thorium mantles do burn brighter and hotter than the newer yttrium mantles. My converted Coleman Quick-Lite table lamp on alcohol produces 100 watts-worth of light with an old-time thorium Silk-Lite No. 21A mantle but only 75 watts-worth with a modern yttrium #21 mantle.

Old-time thorium mantles are still available on eBay. Thorium mantles are not illegal to buy, sell, own, make, or use.

You do need to use some common sense with thorium mantles. You should not eat them. In fact, you may want to wash your hands after installing them rather than licking your fingers.

■ ABOVE: *All Coleman mantles branded 'Silk-Lite' are of the old thorium type and are no longer made. Pictured here is a Silk-Lite No. 21A that would have been used before 1980.* ■

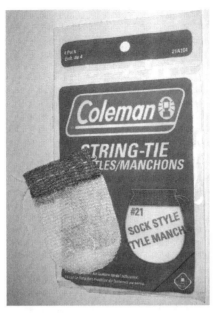

■ **ABOVE:** *The yttrium #21 (what Walmart sells today) replaced the thorium Silk-Lite No. 21A.* ■

As regards sizes, in the thorium world of yesteryear, Coleman sizes (small to large) were Silk-Lite No. 20, Silk-Lite No. 21A, Silk-Lite No. 999, and Silk-Lite No. 1111. In today's yttrium world, the corresponding Coleman sizes (small to large) are #20, #21, #99, and #11.

Mantle Radioactivity

I don't want to come across as flippant about the dangers of radioactivity in regard to mantles but exactly how 'radioactive' is *radioactive*? It needs to be put in context.

A 'Roentgen Equivalent in Man' (abbreviated rem) is a measure of radiation. A millirem (abbreviated mrem) = $1/_{1000}$ rem.

Ramsar, Iran has the world's highest background radiation with some houses receiving 36 mrem per day. That's the *daily* mrem equivalent of the *annual* 132 mSv (milliSieverts) cited on-line.
http://ecolo.org/documents/documents_in_english/ramsar-natural-radioactivity/ramsar.html.

For most of us, located at a distance from Ramsar, background radiation is around one mrem per day, not 36.

A dental X-ray is equivalent to 0.5 mrem. A mammogram is equivalent to 300 mrem.

The Nuclear Regulatory Commission publication *Systematic Radiological Assessment of Exemptions for Source and Byproduct Materials (NUREG-1717)* estimates that 'avid campers' (making 26 two-day camping trips per year, loading the car, riding in the car, changing mantles, etc., and using Coleman-type lanterns **with thorium mantles**) receive 0.05 to 6 mrem per year.
http://www.nrc.gov/reading-rm/doc-collections/nuregs/staff/sr1717/nureg-1717.pdf

Let's sidestep all the tongue-twisters and express this in more thinkable units: dollars.

Background radiation is $1 per day.

Eating a banana is 10¢ additional. A dental X-ray is 50¢. A flight from New York to Los Angeles is $4. A mammogram is $300.

An 'avid camper' would receive $365 per year in background radiation plus somewhere between 5¢ and $6 per year from thorium mantles. Unless the camper in question lived in Ramsar, Iran, in which case background radiation alone would be $13,000 per year.

Hopefully this helps quantify the risk posed by thorium mantles. There is a risk but, in my opinion, the operative word is *small*.

Firing

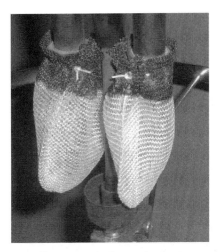

■ **ABOVE:** *New mantles mounted on a lantern, ready for firing.* ■

New mantles must be 'fired' before they will produce light. The factory-applied lacquer must be burned off. All that remains after firing is the ash of the cloth carrier and the rare earth. As you can imagine, mantles are rather delicate creatures.

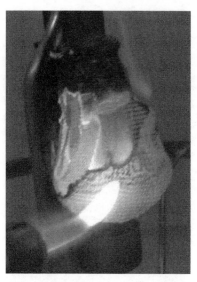

■ **ABOVE:** *A mantle being fired. The flame is from my torch.* ■

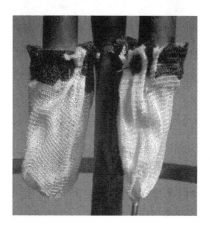

■ **ABOVE:** *Newly fired mantles are flaccid and limpy. It is recommended by one and all that firing be done outdoors so as to avoid inhaling the smoke (particularly with the older radioactive mantles). What nobody tells you, however, is that a mild breeze will break your newly fired mantles. It happens quickly, without warning. So 'outdoors' really means 'outdoors but sheltered from the wind.'* ■

27

■ **ABOVE:** *When you first turn on the pressurized fuel and light the newly-burned-off mantle, it puffs up like a tiny egg-shaped balloon and becomes rigid, holding its shape thereafter.* ■

Generators

In the context of pressure lanterns, the term 'generator' confuses people. Having been raised in the age of electricity, when someone says 'generator,' what jumps to mind is a mass of windings, brushes, and capacitors.

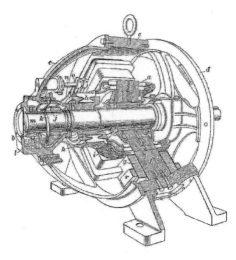

■ **ABOVE:** *An electrical generator, cutaway view. "D.-C. Motors and Generators" by Scott Hancock, 1941, page 36* ■

So let's demystify. To do so, we must return to Eighth Grade science. If you remember, we need three things for a fire: (1) fuel, (2) oxygen, and (3) kindling temperature.

But before fuel will combine with oxygen and ignite, it must be in a gaseous state. Liquid fuel must be converted to a gas so that it can mix with gaseous oxygen. In the lantern world, that's the purpose of the generator. To take liquid fuel and convert it to gaseous fuel. To 'generate' a gas from a liquid.

A steam jenny (in the steam-engine world) performs a similar function. 'Jenny' is slang for generator. A steam generator 'generates' gaseous steam from liquid water. A simple teakettle is a steam jenny.

And the generator for a Coleman lantern is little more than a length of brass tubing. Liquid fuel enters one end of the tube (under pressure that we pumped into the fuel tank). Heat is applied to the outside of the tube. The liquid inside the tube boils and turns to a gas. Gaseous fumes exit the other end of the tube. Gas (in the 'solid-liquid-gas' sense of things) has been *generated* from a liquid.

Combustible Vs. Flammable

'Flash point' is the lowest temperature at which a fuel will ignite in air. OSHA defines a *combustible* liquid as "any liquid having a flash point at or above 100° F." A *flammable* liquid has a flash point below 100° F.

A flammable liquid (gasoline) thus takes fire more easily than a combustible liquid (kero). Spill some kerosene and you make a mess; spill some gas and you burn down the house.

Depending on grade, the flash point of (combustible) kerosene ranges from 100° F to 150° F (per the Phillips 66 MSDS #682950 that you can view on-line: http://www.coastoil.com/MSDS/Phillips%2066%20(Conoco)/Kerosene.pdf).

The flash point of (flammable) gasoline is –45° F. The flash point of white gas (Coleman fuel) is –40% F. That's 40 degrees *below zero*.

How about alcohol?

The flash point of alcohol is below room temperature, ranging from 45° to 63° F.

Methanol is 52° F. Ethanol is 63° F. Isopropyl (91%) is 57° F. Denatured is between 45° F and 55° F. All of the alcohols are thus, by definition, *flammable* albeit less flammable than Coleman fuel.

Preheating

■ **ABOVE:** *And this, Johnny, is why you should never light a liquid-fueled pressure lantern indoors. It's called a 'flare-up.' It's caused by insufficient preheating. Unfortunately, just about every YouTube video demonstrating 'how to light a lantern' shows the procedure taking place at the kitchen sink or on a cluttered workbench out in the shop. Now riddle me this. How will setting the kitchen curtains on fire in the middle of a blackout make life easier?* ■

No liquid-fuel pressure lamp or lantern is immune from flare-ups. Flare-ups are less frequent with gas or alcohol-fueled lanterns (compared to kerosene lanterns) because gas and alcohol are more volatile and vaporize inside the generator more readily than kerosene. But flare-ups do happen with gas and alcohol. Trust me.

Given the traditional Coleman design, should a flare-up occur, just turn off the fuel shutoff valve and be patient. The excess fuel will burn itself out and the flames will dwindle away. In fact, the flare-up might do your desired preheating; at the end of the flare-up, the lamp might actually settle down and operate properly. If so, turn the fuel back on and go about your business. (But, really and truly, it's not the recommended way.)

Candlepower & Watts

Lumens are a measure of the total amount of light emitted by a source in all directions.

Candlepower is a measure of illumination emitted in one direction. One candlepower in all directions produces 12.57 lumens (for the mathematically inclined, 12.57 is equivalent to '4 pi' and 'pi' is the ratio of a circle's circumference to its diameter).

A common incandescent light bulb throws off light in all directions. One *watt* of electrical input produces 15 lumens of light output.

A **100-watt** light bulb thus produces 1500 lumens (100 x 15 = 1500) or **119 candlepower** (1500 ÷ 12.57 = 119). We've gone from *watts* to *lumens* to *candlepower*.

Similarly, a **40-candlepower** mantle produces 502.8 lumens (40 x 12.57 = 502.8) or **33.5 watts** (502.8 ÷ 15 = 33.5). We've gone in reverse order from *candlepower* to *lumens* to *watts*.

As a practical matter, I compare lamps and lanterns using *watts* as the measure of illumination. Including 3-way bulbs, I have a fair range of light bulb wattages for visual comparison (4, 5, 7, 7½, 15, 25, 30, 40, 50, 60, 70, 75, 100, 135, 150, 200, 240, 250, and 300).

It's a simple, real-world approach. When in doubt, I call in the neighbor's kid for a second opinion.

■ **ABOVE:** *The neighbor's kid.* ■

EUROPEAN ALCOHOL LAMPS

Primus

■ **ABOVE:** *Photo courtesy LAMBIT.* ■

World War Two saw rationing of petroleum products. And it was far more strict in Europe than here in the U.S.A. As a consequence of the regulations, European farmers made high-proof moonshine whiskey for use as fuel in mantle-type lanterns. Primus, a Swedish brand of pressure lantern similar to Coleman, made several alcohol-fueled models. Or spirit-fueled, if you will. Or sprit-fueled, as the Swedes spell it.

Today, Primus "sprit" lanterns are both rare and expensive. The lantern pictured above (a Primus Model 1381) recently appeared on eBay. It received 30 bids and sold for $559 including shipping. I don't know about you, but on my budget that puts Primus alcohol-burning lanterns clearly in the collectible camp. A Primus alcohol lantern would not be practical for day-to-day lighting because one bump and/or one dent would take a couple hundred dollars off the resale value.

To make matters worse, after World War II many of these alcohol-burning lanterns were converted to kerosene. So, although a lantern might have been designed for "sprit" and built for "sprit" and have "sprit" stamped into its fuel tank, it is, today, a kerosene lantern. It is not (necessarily) an alcohol lantern regardless of what is stamped on its font or what the seller thinks it is. *Caveat emptor.* Buyer beware.

■ ABOVE: *I knew the Primus 1320 to be a "sprit" or alcohol model and so was surprised to see a 1320 listed for sale as a "kerosene" lantern. But then I noticed the badge had been smudged to make the word "sprit" illegible. It finally dawned on me that it really was, as advertised, a kerosene lantern – an alcohol lantern that had been converted to kerosene after the war.* ■

Gravity-Feed Hanging Lamps

Alcohol's lineage in lighting goes back further than World War Two. Alcohol-burning mantle lamps actually predate World War One. The early lamps often burned white gas as well as alcohol. It was all about the tip, 'bout the tip, 'bout the tip. Tip size determined the fuel-air ratio.

■ **ABOVE:** *Circa 1910, Ehrich & Graetz, Berlin, made an alcohol table lamp called the Rustikus and a hanging ceiling lamp called the Graetzin-Licht. There's a YouTube video showing a Graetzin-Licht operating on alcohol. (At least that's what I think it shows. The commentary is all in German.)*
https://www.youtube.com/watch?v=KO7OoMfCxMw ■

■ **ABOVE:** *This is an ad for a German hanging mantle-lamp from before World War One. It burned 'spirits' (alcohol).* ■

In addition to Gebrüder Lauterbach, Berlin, and his Marla-brand hanging lamp, Jakob Hirschorn, Berlin, made an alcohol hanging lamp branded AIDA Bonares. And the Radius Model 107 was a Swedish-made hanging alcohol lamp. There were others.

But none were as popular as the Tito-Landi lamps of Paris, France. They, too, were on the market before 1910. (The cover of this book is a Tito-Landi magazine ad from 1931.)

Auguste Tito-Landi died in 1947 but his company continued to sell alcohol lamps into the 1970's.

Titus Tito-Landi

■ **ABOVE:** *A Titus alcohol lamp. Empty, this lamp without a shade weighs nearly five pounds. Marble, cranberry glass, brass, pewter, and 100 watts-worth of light. What's not to like?* ■

If you sort it all out and glue it back together, The International Guild of Lamp Researchers has 60+ pages of text and images on alcohol-burning lamps.
www.lampguild.org

Aside. The Guild's archive contains a million words, literally, of lamp info. *All kinds* of lamps. If you have questions on early lamps, for sure pay them a visit.

Much of the Guild information on alcohol-burning lamps involves Tito-Landi. 'Ara in Paris' appears to be the Guild's spiritual authority on all things Tito-Landi. 'Ara in Paris' is the online penname for Ara Kebapcioglu: http://lumiara.perso.neuf.fr/lumiara/en/titusen.htm

These lamps are usually referred to as Tito-Landi but sometimes they're called Tutus lamps. Or Titus-Tito. Or Titus Tito-Landi. What's the difference? I do not know. But, by whatever name, the alcohol Titus-Landi lamps generate 120-200 candlepower depending on the model. In electric-light-bulb terms, 120 candlepower equals 100 watts. Depending on the tip, Tito-Landi lamps burned either alcohol or gasoline (both flammable). None burned kerosene (combustible).

Guild Question No. 1310

On Jul. 30, 2001, Ara in Paris (Lumiara@aol.com) wrote: "The Titus-Lamps . . . are very common in France, but you must . . . check if the lamp you have is made for spirit [alcohol] or gasoline . . . One can't tell at a distance, and it is not easy to tell anyway, even if you're in front of the lamp [because, in operation, the tip or jet cannot be seen]... Then, you must have the small fork (mantle-holder) that fits into the hole in the tube above the center of the burner. It looks like a nail, but ending like a fork. The fork holds an incandescent mantle very hard to find today..."

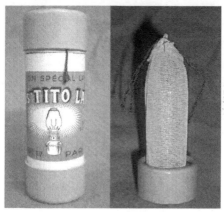

■ **ABOVE:** *"Very hard to find" indeed. Tito-Landi mantles are, today, museum pieces; even photographs are rare. Above we see an authentic Tito-Landi mantle but, in real life, to burn a Titus lamp, we would have to jerry-rig something from other lanterns. Images courtesy Torsten Scherning at* http://scherning.udicom.de/lampen/Tito_Landi_33.htm ■

Dirk Frieborg says, "Since the meeting in Delbrück this year [2008] . . . [I returned home with] two original mantles for Titolandi with me. Now I have decided to open a package and to take the mantle into operation. One might beat me for it, cursing . . ."
http://www.lampenmaxe.de/titolanterni.php

But we digress. 'Ara in Paris' continues: "To pre-heat the burner, you must first open the valve and heat the burner tube with . . . an asbestos prong made for that purpose . . . dip it in SPIRIT (spirit, even if the fuel inside the font is gasoline . . . Caution: all this is VERY dangerous, I don't advise you to light your lamps, if you're not an experienced lamper!!!). The asbestos prong is introduced through two large openings at the side of the gallery and as soon as you hear the vapor come out of the burner, you light the lamp from the top of the straight cylindrical chimney. Good luck!"

Sounds like an exciting afternoon, eh?

■ **ABOVE:** *Preheating the burner. The "sprung fork device" (as Isdale terms it) is shown at the bottom of the photo. It has been soaked in alcohol, lit, and inserted into the side openings of the gallery. Unfortunately, the alcohol preheat flame does not show well in a black-and-white image. Note the improvised mantle. Image courtesy Dirk Frieborg.* ■

There are videos on YouTube that demonstrate the lighting of Tito-Landi lamps. Most are on gasoline-burners but this one is on alcohol. It's interesting to say the least:
https://www.youtube.com/watch?v=Gi__CwFbaTY

Following is the best explanation I've seen on how the Tito-Landi works. I've inserted letters into Isdale's text following which are some marked up images with corresponding letters.

Guild Question #2507
On Oct. 20, 2003 @ 06:34, Robert Isdale.
(robev@zip.com.au) wrote:
"The fuel will travel through the wick **[A]** via capilliary attraction, and in the top point of the wick, within the metal tube **[B]**, it will be vapourised by the heat saturating downwards from the mantle above, hanging on that forked stem **[F]**. This fuel vapour, now under slight pressure, passes through the jet **[J]** in the top of the tube, mixes with air from the side holes **[L]**, and with the aid of the metal gauze **[K]** in the top of the tube, it becomes a bunsen flame capable of incandescing a mantle. Preheating on the Tito Landi is done with sprung fork device, not unlike the Tilly system. Asbestos (or its modern replacement) on the fork is saturated with methylated spirits, and a minute or so of pre-heating will get the process started."

On Oct. 20, 2003, Ara in Paris (Lumiara@aol.com) added:

"Dear all, Rob Isdale's explanations are perfect, I have not much to add."

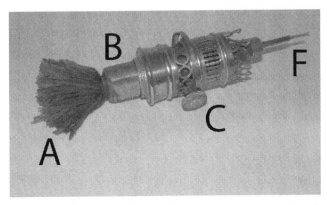

■ **ABOVE:** *A* = *wick or wick bundle,* *B* = *metal tube,* *C* = *shut-off valve,* *F* = *forked stem. The knob "C" does not raise and lower the wick. It is a shut-off valve (needle valve) operating at right angles to the tip or jet.* ■

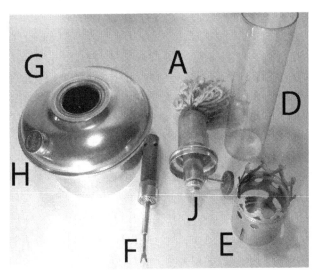

■ **ABOVE:** *A* = *wick,* *D* = *chimney or cylinder,* *E* = *gallery,* *F* = *fork,* *G* = *font,* *H* = *filler cap,* *J* = *tip or "jet." The chimney "D" is*

not bulged but is a straight-sided cylinder, 6" to 8" long with an OD (outside diameter) of 1$^{15}/_{16}$". Most collectors have chimneys made locally by glass blowers. The fork "F" (that holds the mantle) can be improvised from a common nail. Image courtesy Yves Blandeau, Carquefou, Pays de la Loire, France métropolitaine. ∎

∎ **ABOVE:** *J = the tip or "jet." The jet is .0118-.0157" for gas and .0276-.0315" inches for alcohol (as a point of reference, $^1/_{32}$ = .03125). Jet size is the fundamental difference between a Tito-Landi alcohol lamp and a Tito-Landi gas lamp. ∎*

∎ **ABOVE:** At the top of the image, *'Ara in Paris'* calls the vertical stem that holds the fork a "heat transfer rod" or a "recuperator-rod." Isdale refers to the perforated disk *[K]* around the base of the stem as "metal gauze." At the bottom of the image, *L* is what Isdale terms "side holes." ∎

45

■ **ABOVE Left:** *The light from a Tito-Landi mantle. Image courtesy Erwin Schäfer at erwin_sch@freenet.de.* **ABOVE Right:** *The flame under the mantle. Image courtesy Torsten Scherning.* ■

One key to the successful operation of a Tito-Landi lamp is the packing of the wick strands into a bundle. I suspect that squeezing the strands too tightly chokes off the capillary action. But too loose a pack results in 'blowback' into the font; the heated (hence slightly pressurized) fuel vapor finds the path back into the font easier than the path you want it to take out through the jet.

Let us be clear. It is not the *flame* that travels back to the font. The flame is north of the jet, outside the metal chamber that contains vaporized fuel. (The vaporized fuel in the chamber is hot, just like steam is hot and water is cold.) The chamber containing hot vaporized fuel is inside the metal tube, south of the flame and south of the jet. The wick bundle is south of the chamber. Liquid fuel is south of the wick bundle.

Guild Question No. 4247

On Feb. 12, 2007, Chuck Hays (ponybike@hotmail.com) wrote: "As the heat from the preheat alcohol reaches into the burner, vapourized fuel comes out the jet and ignites. Or at least that's the theory. I'm still battling getting the wick packed tightly enough to prevent hot vapour from blowing back into the font." And on Feb. 14: "I did actually have one of the HS#2s burning for a while, but I had to take some extraordinary measures to keep the font cool due to vapour blowback past the wicking bundle."

Newer Tito-Landi lamps ('newer' is relative) have a "small tube [starting in the air space above the fuel but exiting the bottom of the font] that allows gas to escape in case of overpressure due to heat." The 1923 patent (in German) for that small "depressurizing tube" can be seen at: http://www.lampenkueche.de/tlp/Verbesserung%20der%20Entlu eftung%201922.pdf

In earlier models the filler cap was pierced with a small hole for the purpose of relieving overpressure from overheating. This info courtesy Michel at: http://metronius.free.fr/Lampes_m3b.htm.

In practice, the exit end of the patented "depressurizing tube" looks like a small hole (facing downwards) in the bottom of the font. It puts escaping (and flammable) vapor as far away as possible from the glowing mantle. The hole-in-the-filler-cap method of relieving pressure puts escaping vapor much closer to the flame.

QUICK-LIGHT CONVERSION

■ **ABOVE:** *A Coleman Quick-Lite Table lamp circa 1925. Your most reliable source to find one of these lamps is likely eBay.* ■

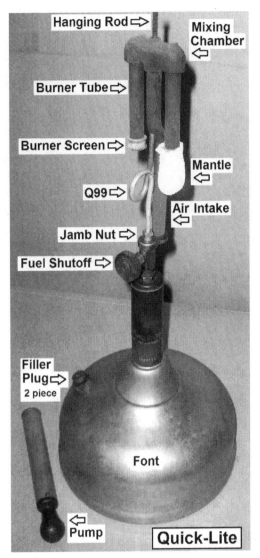

Hanging Rod ⇨

Mixing Chamber ⇦

Burner Tube ⇨

Burner Screen ⇨

Mantle ⇦

Q99 ⇨

Air Intake ⇦

Jamb Nut ⇨

Fuel Shutoff ⇨

Filler Plug ⇨
2 piece

Font

⇦ Pump

Quick-Lite

■ **ABOVE:** *More details on what a Quick-Lite is and how it works can be found in* "Book 5: Coleman Gas Lanterns" *of The Non-Electric Lighting Series. Internet lampers' forums and Coleman directions (that came with the original lamp) are other sources of info.* ■

The Quick-Lite Generator

The Coleman Quick-Lite table lamp used three different generators over the years: the Q77, the Q99, and the R55.

■ **ABOVE:** *The Q77, a super-simple generator. If the Q77 got plugged for any reason you had to turn off the lamp, allow it to cool, and unscrew/remove the generator from the lamp in order to clean it.* ■

TIP from back in the day: Dirty fuel can be filtered through a piece of chamois leather. (It works great BTW.)

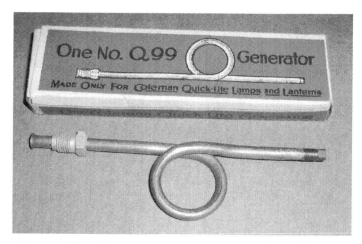

■ **ABOVE:** *The Q77 was superseded by the Q99 with its distinctive loop. The loop created a big surface area. Two wooden kitchen matches burning side by side were sufficient to preheat a Quick-Lite lamp (on Coleman fuel) and get the lamp started.* ■

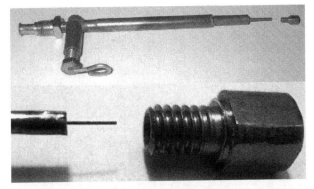

■ **ABOVE:** *The newer R55 is our generator of choice when converting a Quick-Lite lamp to alcohol. It has an internal needle or pricker to clean out the hole in the tip. The pricker can be activated while the generator is mounted on the lamp and the lamp is running. A 90-year-old lamp is sure to have a lot of crud and corrosion in the tank. We really and truly need the R55 generator with the built-in pricker.* ■

The Butterfly Valve

■ **ABOVE:** *This is the air intake tube as seen from below. This is where we'll regulate air flow to the mixing chamber.* ■

■ **ABOVE**: *This is what it will look like when we're done. We're installing a homemade butterfly valve in the air intake tube to adjust the fuel-air ratio as needed.* ■

■ **ABOVE**: *The cotter pin, the main stem for our butterfly valve, has a burr on its long leg. The burr was generated when the cotter pin was manufactured.* ■

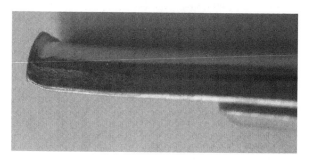

■ **ABOVE**: *Here's a close-up of the burr.* ■

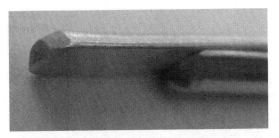

■ **ABOVE**: *The burr must be removed (via grinding wheel, file, or sandpaper).* ■

■ **ABOVE**: *Our butterfly valve is simply a disk of metal $^3/_8"$ in diameter (from a tin can), held in the grip of a cotter pin.* ■

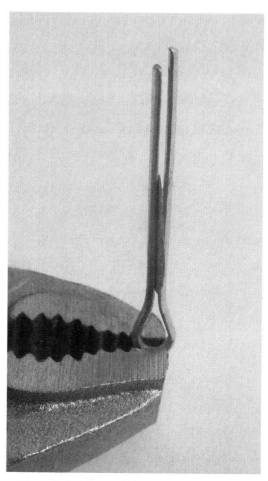

■ **ABOVE:** *The disk is held in place by friction alone. The thickness of the disk spreads the legs of the cotter pin. The two holes that hold the cotter pin in place (which we drill into the air intake tube) are as close as possible to the diameter of the cotter pin; they pinch the legs together and trap the disk, holding it in place. In my first try, incidentally, I used metal from an aluminum beer can for the disk and it was too thin; after assembly, the disk kept falling out of the crack between the cotter pin's legs. Thicker metal from the lid of a soup can worked fine.* ■

■ **ABOVE:** *After the cotter pin is (1) inserted and (2) gripping the disc, its legs are spread to prevent it from moving backwards and coming loose.* ■

■ **ABOVE:** *Hole size is critical. I suggest you drill several trial holes in scrap material and insert your cotter pin into them. By trial-and-error, find the tightest fit possible.* ■

■ **ABOVE:** *You'll probably need access to a set of jobbers drills to get the exact size. In my case, a #49 drill bit (.073" in diameter) worked best.* ■

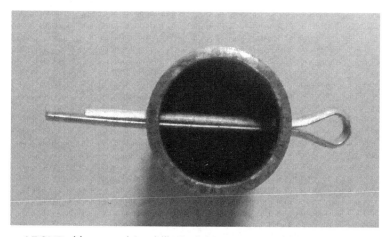

■ **ABOVE:** *You need to drill straight across and bisect the circle formed by the air tube.* ■

■ **ABOVE:** *Simultaneously, you need to drill a 'level' hole, for lack of a better term. This is tricky with a hand-held drill but doable. Maybe you should practice on a couple of pieces of scrap tubing first before attacking the actual air intake tube on the lamp itself. Brace up! Faint heart ne'er won fair maiden.* ■

■ **ABOVE:** *To assemble the butterfly valve, first poke* **one** *leg (only) of the cotter pin through* **both** *holes in the air intake tube. Then twist the cotter pin so that its crack faces the tube's opening.* ■

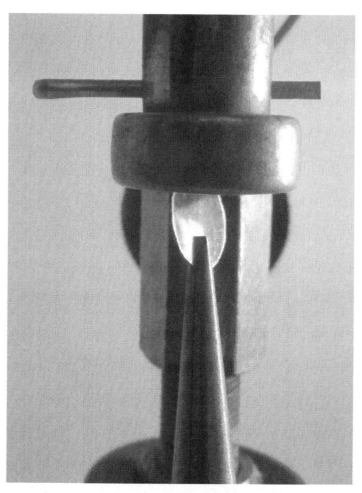

■ **ABOVE:** *With needlenose pliers, insert the metal disk into the mouth of the air intake tube and into the crack of the cotter pin. Then (and this is the hardest part of all), pinch the legs of the cotter pin together (using the pliers) and slide the second (shorter) leg of the cotter pin through the hole in the sidewall of the air tube. This takes 2-5 minutes of fussin' around during which time you are absolutely forbidden to shout rude and blasphemous things at your lantern or at me for suggesting this to you. No exceptions. Praise the Lord.* ■

■ **ABOVE:** *Spread the legs of the cotter pin so that it is trapped in position.* ■

■ **ABOVE:** *See? Wasn't that fun?* ■

■ **ABOVE:** *You now have a lamp that will (given Silk-Lite No. 21A mantles and 91% isopropyl rubbing alcohol) produce light on par with a 100-watt electric light bulb. Any 10" (diameter) glass shade will fit. The shade shown here is from a Rayo kerosene lamp, not a Coleman Quick-Lite.* ■

Operating a Quick-Lite

Quick-Lites are 75-100 years old. If you have one, check it over before attempting to light it. First, does it hold pressure? Pump it up and hold it underwater. A 5-gallon contractor's bucket or a laundry-room sink works well to hold the water. A stream of bubbles reveals a pressure leak. DON'T LIGHT a lamp with a pressure leak.

Next, clean out the fuel tank (font). This is best done by putting some lead BB's in the tank along with some fuel and shaking vigorously. It knocks loose tons of crud and corrosion. Shotgun shells and lead fishing sinkers and pellet-gun pellets are all good sources of lead BB's.

Put half a cup of BB's in the fuel tank (a funnel helps). Pour in some fuel and shake. Pour out the dirty fuel. Pour in more clean fuel. Shake. Repeat. Repeat. Repeat. Please know that, at the end, it will take lots of patient jiggling with the lamp upside down to get all the BB's back out. But the tank will be clean.

Replace the small screens in the burner tubes if need be. I bought some screens on eBay (search for "coleman burner screen") from Kelly Williams in Frankfort, Indiana.

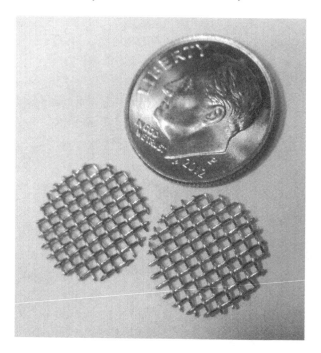

TIP: If you remove the burner tubes, the best penetrating oil around (for lack of a better term) is a 50/50 mix of acetone and automatic transmission fluid. The components don't go in solution worth a darn (so you have to keep shaking it) but it works better than anything else I've ever seen. Hat tip to The International Guild of Lamp Researchers for this one.

If the burner tubes don't unscrew immediately, don't force the issue. They are annealed brass (from previous burning in years past) which means they are soft and will bend easily. Soak the top end of the lamp overnight in penetrating oil to help loosen them.

*****

Coleman Warning

I've attended enough boardroom meetings in my life to appreciate this wouldn't be the great nation it is without a few 'CYA' (Cover Your Fanny) statements. The following is from Coleman. Well, Coleman's lawyers, actually. The purpose of which is to hold Coleman innocent in the event a Coleman customer colors outside the lines and something goes awry. So please be advised:

> **"Warning**
>
> "Coleman replacement parts are intended for use only on specific Coleman products. Any other use of Coleman replacement parts is strictly prohibited. *Use of Coleman replacement parts on the wrong Coleman product, or for non-approved applications, may cause poor product performance and can cause serious personal injury, property damage or death."* [emphasis theirs]
> www.coleman.com/coleman/parts/parts_lantern.asp

Next, before running your Quick-Lite on alcohol, run it on Coleman fuel – what it was designed for. If you fail to do so, and your lamp gives problems, you won't know for sure if the conversion is to blame or the lamp itself is to blame. Please take it one step at a time. Make sure you have a lamp that works properly on the fuel it was designed for before investing your time in a conversion.

For the actual lamp operation, the steps are these:

(1) Fill the lantern with fuel.

(2) Snug down the fill cap with a wrench. The washer for the fill cap is lead, not rubber. The wrench size is $^{13}/_{16}$".

(3) Loosen the inner air stem a couple of turns to receive the external pump.

You'll find the air stem on old Quick-Lites is sometimes messed up, drilled out in years gone by to accept a bicycle pump or compressed air hose or CO_2 cylinder or similar device. It's something to look for during the initial purchase of your lamp.

(4) Pump in some pressure (30 strokes, say) and tighten the hollow air stem (finger tight).

(5) Tie on the mantles and fire them. When burning alcohol as fuel you'll get the best results (on the Quick-Lite) with Coleman Silk-Lite No. 21A mantles. 'Firing' means burning off the mantles' lacquer coating with matches or a torch. Outside please.

■ **ABOVE:** *A butane soldering torch works well for firing the mantles as well as preheating the generator.* ■

(6) Preheat the lamp. There's already pressure in the font (from step #4, above) so, before you start preheating, give the on-off valve a quick back-and-forth twist to squirt a bit of fuel into the generator.

Preheating is easiest done with a butane soldering torch (although a propane or alcohol torch will also work). Likely you'll use the same torch you used earlier for firing the mantles.

'Play' the flame of the torch on the generator. Keep the torch moving i.e. let's not melt a hole in the generator. Make sure the cleaning 'lever' (tiny crank) on the generator is 'up' in its 'open' position and allows vaporized fuel to exit the generator. (This assumes you have the R55 generator described earlier.)

(7) When the fuel (the first squirt that we provided) boils inside the generator, gas vapor will come out the nozzle, take fire, and the mantles will flare up. That indicates the lamp is preheated or nearly so. Now you can turn on the lantern's fuel valve. Keep the torch in place for a moment until the process becomes self-sustaining and the mantles take over from the torch, vaporizing the fuel as it passes through the generator.

(8) With alcohol, start with the butterfly valve at a 45° angle – half on and half off. As soon as the lantern runs on its own, adjust the butterfly valve as needed to produce the most light. Small pliers work well to turn the cotter pin.

(9) After everything is running smoothly, pump in more pressure.

As mentioned earlier, with 91% isopropyl alcohol as the fuel and Coleman Silk-Lite No. 21A mantles you can expect light output equal to a 100-watt light bulb.

OTHER CONVERSIONS

I found two other pressure lamps (i.e. lamps that are available on the market today, not exotic antiques) that can be converted to burn alcohol. They are the Petromax 150CP lantern and the Leacock Model 107 table lamp.

Are they *safe* on alcohol? The Model 107 is. It was designed for white gas and we're going to run it on alcohol, a less volatile fuel than what it was designed for. White gas evaporates at 40° below zero (F). Alcohol evaporates just below room temperature. That means gas evaporates more readily than alcohol; gas takes fire easier than alcohol; gas is more volatile than alcohol. If the Model 107 is safe on gas then it's safer on alcohol.

The Petromax on alcohol is the other way around. Kerosene is combustible. Alcohol is flammable. The Petromax is a kerosene lantern. On alcohol, the Petromax (a kerosene lantern) is burning a *more* volatile fuel than it was designed for.

If push came to shove, I'm sure I would burn alcohol in a Petromax if the need arose. Like driving a car with one headlight, however, I'd be a wee bit cautious. Or maybe like running an electric table saw. I know more than one person who is missing a finger.

With both of these lamps, air input must be restricted. And please remember that all mantles are not created equal. And all alcohols are not created equal. Methanol, denatured alcohol, and 91% isopropyl each produce different results and must be treated as three distinct fuels.

Leacock Model 107

■ **ABOVE:** *This is the grandson, if you will, of the Coleman Quick-Lite table lamp. It's the Leacock Model 107, available brand new. It has a stainless steel font but still uses an external pump.* ■

The Leacock Model 107 can be purchased at Lehman's (www.lehmans.com) where they call it an "Amish Table Lamp" or from the Leacock Coleman Center in Ronks, PA: http://www.leacockcolemancenter.com/Stainless-Steel-Table-Lamp-Leacock-Lamp-107SS/item/107SS

■ **ABOVE:** *As purchased, the air intake tube on the 107 has a threaded-on choke collar to restrict incoming air and provide the correct fuel-air ratio for white gas. Removing the choke collar let's in more air and allows us to burn kerosene. But what we need for alcohol is LESS air, not more.* ■

■ **ABOVE:** *The hole in the choke collar (stock; straight from the factory) is $\frac{9}{32}$".* ■

■ **ABOVE:** *The hole in the air tube itself is $^{13}/_{32}$" in diameter.* ■

■ **ABOVE:** *I drilled a set of four "washers" (in $^{1}/_{64}$" increments) from $^{1}/_{8}$" down to $^{5}/_{64}$" to act as inserts in the choke collar and further restrict incoming air.* ■

My best result on 91% isopropyl was 75 watts-worth of light. That came from using a Petromax [brand] 150CP mantle plus a washer with a $^1/_8$ " hole.

My best result on denatured alcohol was 40 watts-worth of light. That came from using a Coleman Silk-Lite No. 21A mantle plus a washer with a $^5/_{64}$" hole.

My best result on methanol was 30 watts-worth of light. That came from using a Petromax 150CP mantle plus a washer with a $^1/_8$" hole.

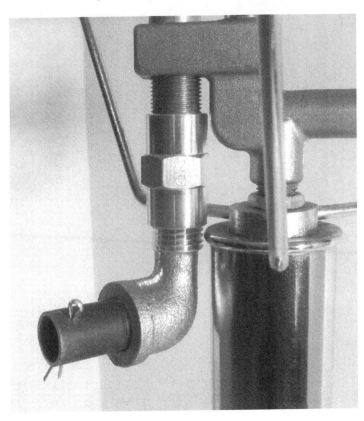

■ **ABOVE:** *I was truly disappointed with this setup. It's a butterfly valve on the 107 (similar to what we installed on the Coleman Quick-Lite). I was expecting great things from the variable adjustment but the best I got on 91% isopropyl plus Silk-Lite 21A mantles was 40 watts-worth of light (exactly the same as what I got with a non-adjustable $^5/_{64}$" washer). Bummer.* ■

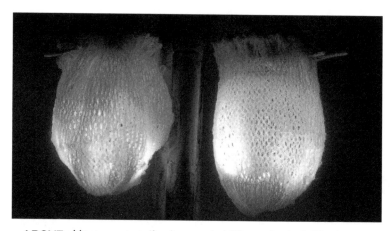

■ **ABOVE:** *Here we see the Leacock 107 on alcohol. The mantles don't fully incandesce; there are brown areas. Even so, 30 or 40 or 75 watts-worth of light (depending on the mantle and/or alcohol in question) is superior to a candle.* ■

Although they look very similar, please know that there are fundamental differences between the Coleman Quick-Lite and the Leacock Model 107. The parts are not interchangeable.

The Quick-Lite generator, for example, be it a Q77, Q99, or R55, fastens to the lamp with a male "jamb nut." The newer Leacock Model 107 uses a Coleman 220 generator (designed for the Model 220/228 lantern but used on several other models as well). The 220 generator fastens to the lamp with a "flare nut." They are simply not compatible, one with the other.

The Petromax 150CP

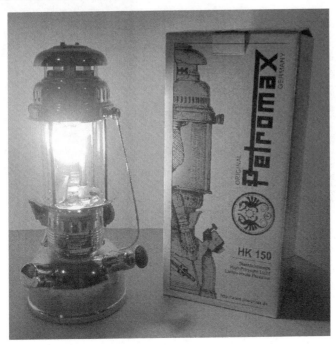

■ **ABOVE:** *The box says* **HK** *150 and not* **CP** *150. 'HK' stands for Hefnerkerze, a German unit of light output from 1890. 'CP' would indicate candlepower. One candlepower = 1.0893 Hefnerkerze. And one Hefnerkerze = 0.9208 candlepower. In common parlance the two terms are close enough that they are often used interchangeably.* ■

The big Petromax lanterns are 500CP whereas the 'baby' Petromax lanterns are 150CP. As used here, when I say "Petromax" I'm including the off-brand Petromax clones as well as the Petromax brand itself.

The 150CP lanterns can be readily adjusted to burn 91% isopropyl but the larger 500CP lanterns cannot. The reason is simple.

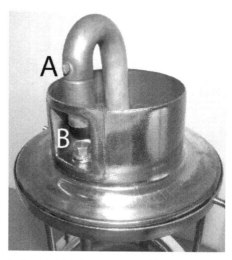

■ **ABOVE:** *This is a 500CP Petromax. If we remove the ventilator from the top of lantern we get a glimpse of its inner workings. Here we see the U-shaped mixing tube as well as the jet that squirts vaporized fuel upwards into the mixing tube. Air is sucked sideways into the mixing tube at the gap [B] between the jet and the tube.* ■

■ **ABOVE:** *This is a 150CP Petromax. To burn alcohol we need to reduce air input. This is done by lowering the U-shaped mixing tube and shrinking the gap between the end of the tube and the jet. Here we see the threaded end of the mixing tube at the top and, at the bottom, the hole in the inner casing through which the jet will be inserted.* ■

■ **ABOVE:** *This is a 150CP Petromax. When the inner casing is mounted on the lantern, the jet sticks up through the hole in the floor of the inner casing. To burn alcohol we lower the U-shaped mixing tube until the gap between the end of the tube and the jet is barely $1/16"$.* ■

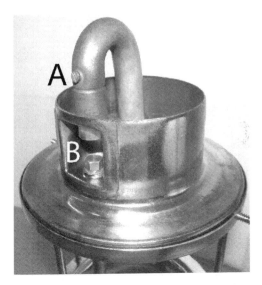

I experimented with both a Petromax (brand) 150CP lantern and a Britelyt (knockoff) 150CP lantern on alcohol. I was surprised to find that, with both lanterns, the only alcohol to burn successfully was 91% isopropyl. The mantles would not incandesce on either methanol or denatured alcohol. Given 91% isopropyl, the results on different mantles were as follows:

Petromax (brand) 150CP mantles: 100 watts-worth of light (you can buy Petromax brand mantles online from Britelyt).

Coleman #20 yttrium mantles: 100 watts-worth of light.

Coleman Silk-Lite No. 20 thorium mantles: 50 watts-worth of light (this is a rare size of mantle).

Coleman #21 yttrium mantles: 75 watts-worth of light.

Coleman Silk-Lite No. 21A thorium mantles: 40 watts-worth of light.

I was surprised that the yttrium mantles produced more light than thorium mantles. I have no explanation. Just reportin' the facts here, folks.

SAFETY

Flammability

In a different time and place and in a different context I wrote: "Perhaps the greatest single danger with Coleman pressure lanterns is the handling and storage of Coleman fuel (white gas) outside the lantern. The lantern itself is a sealed, closed-loop system. Once inside the lantern, Coleman fuel is quite safe. The bigger danger lies with the gas can kicking around in the back of your pickup.

"And refilling a white-gas lantern by the light of another lantern, or by the light of a campfire (read live flame) . . . now *that's* walking with the angels . . ."

But much the same can be said of alcohol. Both Coleman fuel and alcohol are flammable. Both evaporate quickly and give off ignitable fumes at room temperature (or even below room temperature). All it takes is one spark to light up your life. "Look daddy. Go *BOOM!*"

Oxygen Starvation

Outside air is 21% oxygen. Inside air is something below that. You, your wood stove, your birthday candles, your girlfriend, and the family dog all compete for the available oxygen. If the oxygen level is depleted too far you suffer 'oxygen starvation.'

You say you feel 'just fine' even though you are pale and confused. Later, you have no energy/strength/stamina. You have shortness of breath, chest tightness, blue coloring around your lips, tingling fingers, increased pulse, you want to sleep.

The fix is easy. Ditch the girlfriend. Well, okay. Open a window. Let in some fresh air.

Your wood stove has a chimney and is thus 'vented.' Venting gets rid of unwanted byproducts of combustion. Your gas range in the kitchen (typically four burners plus an oven) is not vented. But whether an appliance is vented or not, the oxygen it uses in the burning process comes from the inside air.

Oxygen starvation can also occur at high altitudes (where the air is 'thin') or when breathing mixtures of gases with low oxygen content (e.g. diving).

What are the long-term consequences if you ignore the symptoms of oxygen starvation?

Answer: extreme fatigue, waking at night gasping for breath, loss of eyesight, loss of short term memory, progressive weakening of the heart muscle leading to heart failure.

But that's the long-term extreme. Again, as far as fuel-burning lamps and lanterns are concerned, the fix is easy. Open a window. Let in some fresh air.

Carbon Monoxide

Big topic, this. As a youngster, I was repeatedly lectured on the dangers of carbon monoxide. Why? Because my mother had two schoolmates die from carbon monoxide. It made quite an impression on her tiny high school graduating class of twelve students.

The victims had been out 'parking' in a Model 'A' Ford. To keep warm, they'd left the engine idling and the heater on. Heat for the Model 'A' was pulled from the exhaust manifold. It was a poor design, well known for leaking exhaust gases. In this case it proved fatal.

(You might feel better knowing that, today, a car's heater extracts heat from the hot water in the cooling system, not from the exhaust system.)

Carbon monoxide (CO is the chemical symbol) is produced when something burns with insufficient oxygen being present.

Things that smolder (cigarettes, pipes, incense, cigars, charcoal briquettes) give off carbon monoxide in considerable quantity. That's why it's not safe to use a charcoal grill inside the house. In contrast, things that burn with an open flame produce very little carbon monoxide.

The smoldering concept is simple enough to demonstrate. If you want to test your carbon monoxide detector, bring a burning stick of incense nearby. The detector will inform you of the presence of carbon monoxide in no uncertain terms.

But the smoldering concept can also be confusing. Why does something smolder and not burn? After all, it has oxygen. It has access to the same air that we're breathing.

The answer is that it doesn't have ENOUGH oxygen. Each material has its own threshold of how much oxygen is required to burn with an open flame. Firewood will burn with the amount of oxygen found in the open air. Tobacco will smolder. Steel will not even smolder.

But an oxyacetylene cutting torch doesn't MELT a hole in steel. It BURNS a hole in steel. When you squeeze the lever, pure oxygen is introduced at the welding tip and the steel literally burns.

Think about all the restrictions around medical patients who are on oxygen. Various materials will ignite and burn in a high-oxygen atmosphere that won't burn, or will merely smolder, in our regular atmosphere.

So let me say it again. Carbon monoxide is produced when something burns with insufficient oxygen being present. Insufficient oxygen, that is, for the material at hand, for the material that is smoldering.

There are three ways that a condition of 'insufficient oxygen' can come about.

(1) To burn with an open flame, the fuel in question (tobacco, for example) needs more oxygen than is present in ordinary air. We just covered that.

(2) The device (a stove burner, for example) can be out of adjustment; the fuel/air ratio can be incorrect. With propane, a 'lean' burn (not enough fuel) can be recognized when flames lift away from the burner and tend to go out. A 'rich' burn (too much fuel) results in large yellow flames. (Propane flames should be blue.) Both rich and lean burns reveal incomplete combustion and imply the production of carbon monoxide.

(3) In an enclosed area (room, cellar, shed, house trailer), combustion can deplete the available oxygen with the result that carbon monoxide (CO) is produced as a byproduct of combustion rather than the normally-produced carbon dioxide (CO_2). Carbon dioxide (CO_2) is nontoxic and harmless to breathe.

Note that in this last scenario carbon monoxide can be produced even when the appliances are properly adjusted. When the oxygen is 'depleted' or partially used up it means there's not enough to go around. And in the combustion process it takes less oxygen to make CO (with one oxygen atom) than it does to make CO_2 (with two oxygen atoms). So, in a situation with limited oxygen, CO is what gets made.

The fix, of course, is to crack open a window and let in some fresh air.

Carbon monoxide is colorless, odorless, and tasteless. That's what makes it so dangerous. It sneaks up on you.

Hemoglobin is the principle oxygen-carrying compound in your blood. Unfortunately, the attraction or affinity between CO and hemoglobin is many times stronger than the affinity between oxygen and hemoglobin so CO displaces the oxygen in your bloodstream. Your brain and heart do not get the oxygen that they need.

Sometimes the first symptom of CO poisoning is simply drowsiness. First you sleep, then you cannot be roused from your sleep, then you die.

Headache is another common symptom of acute carbon monoxide poisoning. (Acute means 'brief and severe.') With oxygen depletion you are pale and confused; with carbon monoxide, you have a headache.

Unfortunately, all kinds of confusion exists surrounding lanterns and carbon monoxide. The more I looked, the more brouhaha I found. I decided it was time to shell out a few bucks for a meter and do my own testing.

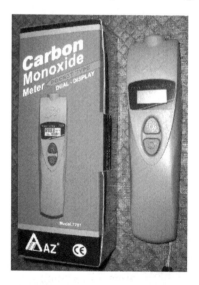

I tested all kinds of lamps and lanterns, one at a time, in a closed room with a CO detector. The detector, factory-preset to 30 ppm (parts per million), never went off. I began to doubt it was even working until I moved a stick of burning incense nearby. Then it *screamed.*

Oops. We need to back up a step and understand parts per million.

One ppm is not very big. A carton of paint at the hardware store holds four one-gallon cans. Visualize, if you will, 17 gallons of paint – a stack of boxes, four high, plus one extra gallon on top. A single drop of paint thinner, measured with an eye-dropper and spread evenly across all 17 gallons, constitutes one part per million.

Okay. Back to the story. Where should I position the detector? Above or below the lamp being tested? It turns out that CO is slightly lighter than air. CO (carbon monoxide) has a mass of $12 + 16 = 28g/mol$, while the mean mass of air is $28.8g/mol$. So the detector, to get a reading, should be positioned *above* the lamp being tested.

I found the most reliable way to get CO readings was to put the lanterns in the bathtub. Atop the shower curtain was a 6" gap between the curtain bar and the shower ceiling. Holding the meter at the gap, just outside the shower (with the shower curtain closed, of course), where the hot/rising gases were spilling out into the bathroom, gave the most consistent readings. Outside the shower, near the ceiling, I could pick up fleeting, transient spikes. At floor level, inside the tub or out, the readings were near zero (after one hour of operation and with the lamp still running). The room itself was 5' x 8' with an 8' ceiling. The meter measured in 1 ppm increments and had a measuring range from zero to 999 ppm. Even after an hour in a closed shower stall (with the bathroom door closed), CO proved to be elusive stuff. Out in general living quarters it was virtually impossible to get a reading.

For petroleum products, the lantern I used was a 1970's Coleman 639-with-pricker (not to be confused with the 639C currently being marketed). It outputs light on par with a 250-watt light bulb. The 639-with-pricker is the only Coleman I've found that will run on white gas AND kerosene AND diesel fuel using today's yttrium mantles. That makes it perfect for comparison testing of fuels.

White gas (Coleman fuel) produced an average reading of 10 ppm CO; a range from 6-to-14 ppm; and transient spikes of 25 ppm.

With the same lantern, kerosene produced an average reading of 16 ppm CO; a range from 12-to-20 ppm; and transient spikes of 39 ppm.

A Rayo wick-type kerosene lamp (not a pressure lamp and having no mantle) produced an average reading of 20 ppm CO; a range from 16-to-24 ppm; and transient spikes of 41 ppm.

A propane mantle lamp produced an average reading of 5 ppm. I didn't think it could get any better than that, frankly, until I tried alcohol.

For alcohol I used the Coleman Quick-Lite conversion described earlier. It's a mantle lamp and produces 100 watts-worth of light. And the results? I could not get a reading. Try as I would, not so much as one ppm. Nothing. Nadda. Zilch.

First-hand experimentation, up close and personal, convinced me that alcohol was the safest fuel for inside use.

You can conduct these tests yourself, of course. That's the beauty of the scientific method. You don't have to take my word for anything.

LIGHTING BOOKS BY RON BROWN

The Non-Electric Lighting Series is available on Amazon in both Kindle ebook and paperback format:

Book 1: Candles

"I got into candle making a few years ago and found the information quite accurate as regards wax." - Ramdrive

Book 2: Olive Oil Lamps &c.

"Awesome book!" – Alison Thompson

Book 3: Lamp Fuels

"I am so pleased to actually get real honest answers. Mr. Brown thank you." – Janncy

Book 4: Kerosene Lamps

"Everyone should read this." – R.L. Ake

Book 5: Coleman Gas Lanterns

"If you collect or use semi-vintage Coleman lanterns you want this book. So much of the information was new to me even after 40 years of using them." – Sharon L. Buman

Book 6: Kerosene Pressure Lanterns

"[In Book 6] Ron discusses Petromax . . . Coleman . . . Aladdin . . . I think it would be wise to have this [whole] set of books tucked away in your reference library." – Gaye Levy, Backdoor Survival

Book 7: Propane for Preppers

"Outstanding article! One of the BEST I've ever read or seen on any preparedness website." – TPS

(Much of the material in Book 7 originally appeared as a series of five articles in the preppers' blog *Backdoor Survival*.)

Book 8: Alcohol Mantle Lamps

"The *Amazing* 2000-Hour Flashlight" and **"The *New* 2000-Hour Flashlight"** are both on Amazon in Kindle and paperback formats.

Regarding **"The *Amazing* 2000-Hour Flashlight"**:
"Perfect." – Virginia Candela

Regarding **"The *New* 2000-Hour Flashlight"**:
"This is a wonderful book. Kudos to Ron Brown." – Brian R

"Lanterns, Lamps & Candles" is a CD (in pdf format) available at www.rc-publishing.com.

"Honestly, it's a 10+. Nothing else comes close. LOVED it." – J.S., Oregon

There's also a (free) YouTube video entitled ***Converting a Gas Lantern to Kerosene***.

"Ron, this is one of the best and most professional videos on YouTube. Your organization, detail, stage presence, and voice are fantastic." – Guiding Mike

49733477R00052

Made in the USA
Lexington, KY
17 February 2016